Go, Trucks, Go!

Written by Sonia Sander
& Illustrated by Rick Courtney

SCHOLASTIC INC.

New York   Toronto   London   Auckland   Sydney
Mexico City   New Delhi   Hong Kong   Buenos Aires

One truck drives
up the main street.
Go, truck, go!

Two **trucks** drive
up the side **streets**.
Go, **trucks**, go!

I am a bulldozer.
I can move a
rock or tree.
Go, bulldozer, go!

I am a dump truck.
I can move **lots** of
rocks and **trees**.
Go, dump truck, go!

I am a front loader.
I am digging a hole.
I will dig three more
holes.

I am a cement mixer.
I can fill all four **holes**.
Go, mixer truck, go!

I am a dump truck.
I can move **lots** of
old **tires**.

The playground is finished with **towers** of **tires**!
Go, **trucks**, go!